KEEP
CALM
AND
PLAY
ON

KEEP
CALM
AND
PLAY
ON

WISE PUBLICATIONS
part of The Music Sales Group

London / New York / Paris / Sydney / Copenhagen / Berlin / Madrid / Hong Kong / Tokyo

Published by
WISE PUBLICATIONS
14-15 Berners Street, London W1T 3LJ,
United Kingdom.

Exclusive Distributors:
MUSIC SALES LIMITED
Distribution Centre, Newmarket Road,
Bury St Edmunds, Suffolk IP33 3YB,
United Kingdom.
MUSIC SALES PTY LIMITED
20 Resolution Drive, Caringbah, NSW 2229,
Australia.

Order No. AM1004938
ISBN 978-1-78038-631-7
This book © Copyright 2012 Wise Publications,
a division of Music Sales Limited.

Edited by Jenni Norey.
Cover designed by Michael Bell Design.
Printed in the EU.

YOUR GUARANTEE OF QUALITY
As publishers, we strive to produce every book to
the highest commercial standards.
This book has been carefully designed to minimise awkward page turns
and to make playing from it a real pleasure.
Particular care has been given to specifying acid-free, neutral-sized
paper made from pulps which have not been elemental chlorine bleached.
This pulp is from farmed sustainable forests and was
produced with special regard for the environment.
Throughout, the printing and binding have been planned to ensure a sturdy,
attractive publication which should give years of enjoyment.
If your copy fails to meet our high standards, please inform us
and we will gladly replace it.

www.musicsales.com

BRIDGE OVER TROUBLED WATER

Words & Music by Paul Simon.

Verse 2
When you're down and out,
When you're on the street,
When evening falls so hard
I will comfort you.
I'll take your part,
Oh, when darkness comes
And pain is all around.

Like a bridge over troubled water *etc.*

BEAUTIFUL

Words & Music by Linda Perry.

1. Ev-'ry day___ is so___
2. To all your friends___ you're de-

14

CHASING CARS

Words & Music by
Gary Lightbody, Nathan Connolly, Tom Simpson,
Paul Wilson & Jonathan Quinn.

here, if I just lay here, would you lie with me and just for-get the world? For-get what we're told be-fore we get too old. Show me a gar-den that's burst-ing in-to life. All that I

things will nev - er change_ for us at all.___ If I lay

here, if I just lay here,_ would you lie

with me___ and___ just for - get the world?_

THE CLOSEST THING TO CRAZY

Words & Music by Mike Batt.

1. How can I think I'm stand-ing strong yet feel the air be-neath my feet?

2. How can you make me fall a-part then break my fall with lov-ing lies?

EVERYWHERE I GO

Words & Music by Lissie Maurus & Curt Schneider.

should know.

could be.

And I fall on my knees.

And I fall on my knees.

Tell me how's the way to go.

Tell me how's the way to be.

Tell me how's the way

Tell me how's the way

to be

to go.

to e-voke some em-pa-thy.

Tell me why I feel so low.

Dan - ger will fol-low me now, ev - 'ry - where I go.

THE FEAR

Words & Music by Lily Allen & Greg Kurstin.

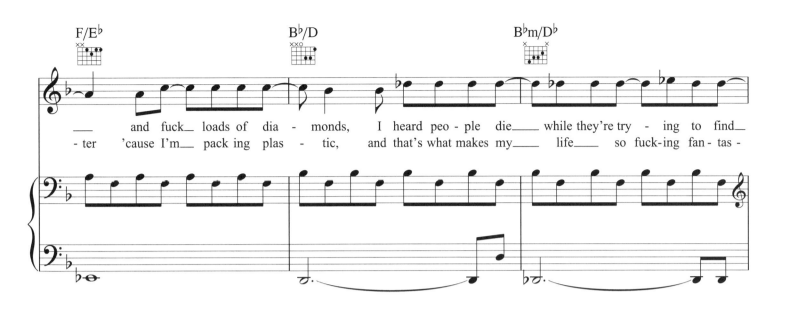

and fuck loads of dia - monds, I heard peo - ple die___ while they're try - ing to find___
-ter 'cause I'm___ pack ing plas - tic, and that's what makes my___ life___ so fuck-ing fan - tas -

___ them. And I'll take my clothes___ off and it will be shame - less, 'cause ev - 'ry - one knows___
- tic. And I am a wea - pon of mas - sive con - sump - tion and it's not my fault___

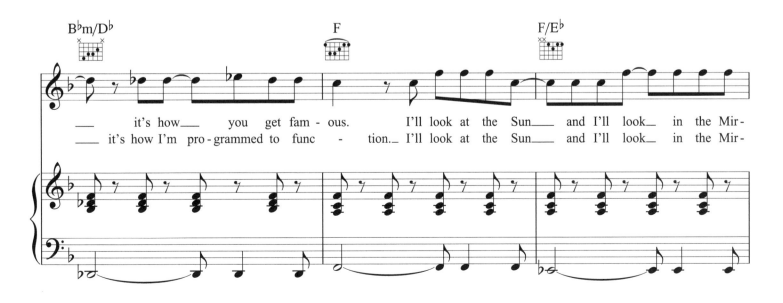

___ it's how___ you get fam - ous. I'll look at the Sun___ and I'll look___ in the Mir -
___ it's how I'm pro - grammed to func - tion.___ I'll look at the Sun___ and I'll look___ in the Mir-

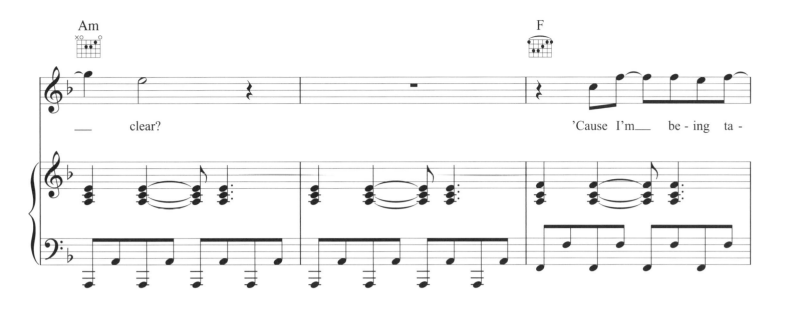

'Cause I'm___ be - ing ta -

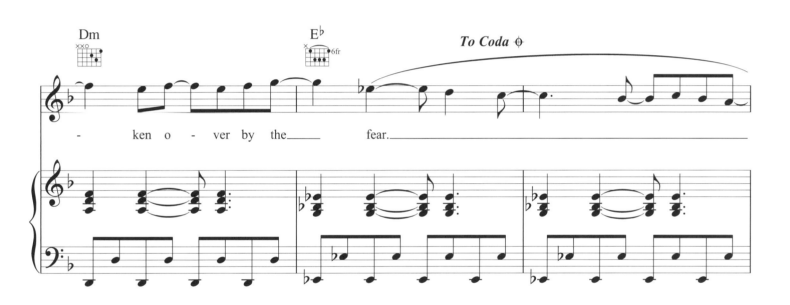

- ken o - ver by the___ fear.___

To Coda ⊕

but I'm not a sin - ner, and ev - 'ry-thing's cool as long as I'm get-ting thin -

- ner. And I don't know

HALLELUJAH

Words & Music by Leonard Cohen.

HEARTBEATS

Words & Music by Olof Dreijer & Karin Dreijer Andersson.

1. One night to be con - fused, one night to speed up truth;
2. One night of ma - gic rush; the start, a sim - ple touch.

we had a prom - ise made, four hands and then a - way.
One night to push and scream, and then re - lief.

HIDE AND SEEK

Words & Music by Imogen Heap.

-pet, sink - ing feel - ing.

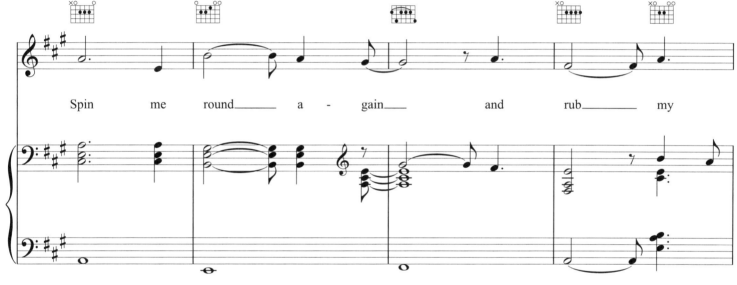

Spin me round____ a - gain____ and rub____ my

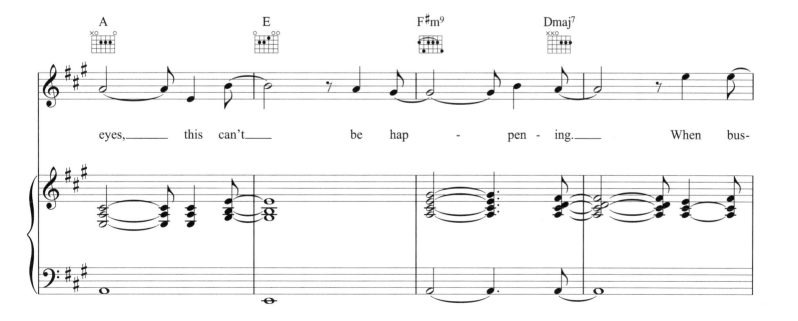

eyes,____ this can't____ be hap - pen - ing.____ When bus-

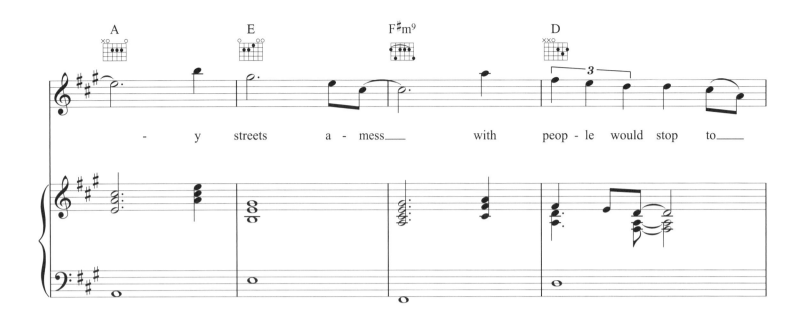

- y streets a - mess____ with peop - le would stop to____

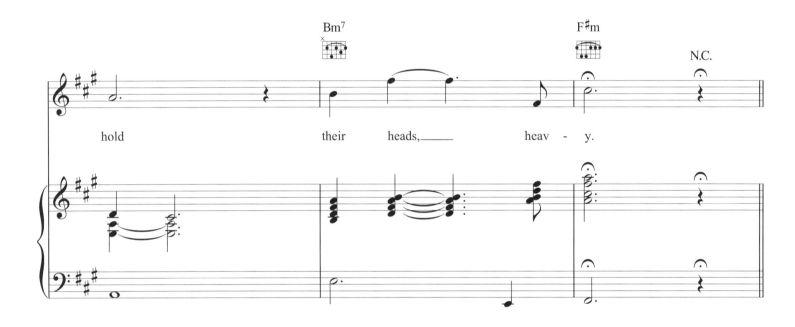

hold their heads,____ heav - y.

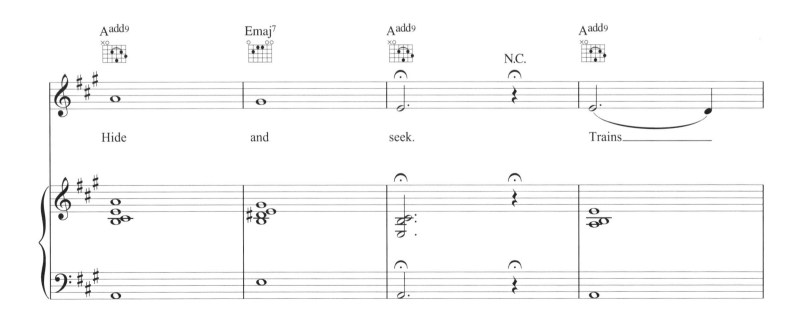

Hide and seek. Trains_____

and sew - ing ma - chines. _____ All those _____ years _____ they were here first. Oil - y

on - ly meant well,_____ well of course you did.__ Mm, what you say?_____ Mm, that it's

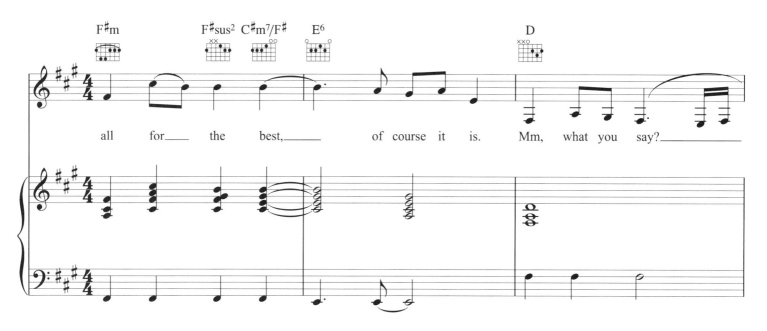

all for____ the best,_____ of course it is. Mm, what you say?_____

That it's just____ what____ we need,_____ and you de - cid - ed this.___

don't care, you don't care a bit. No you, you don't care a bit. Mm,_____

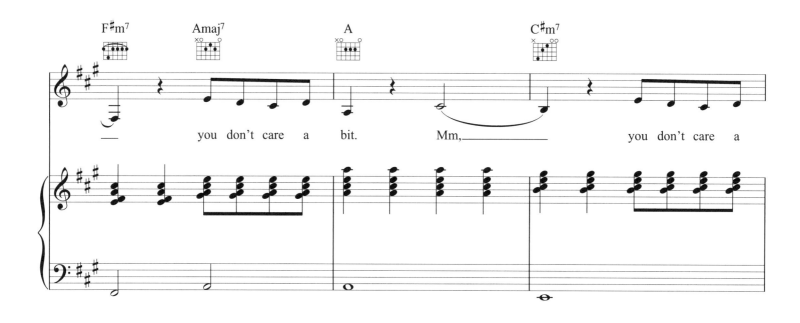

_____ you don't care a bit. Mm,_____ you don't care a

rit.

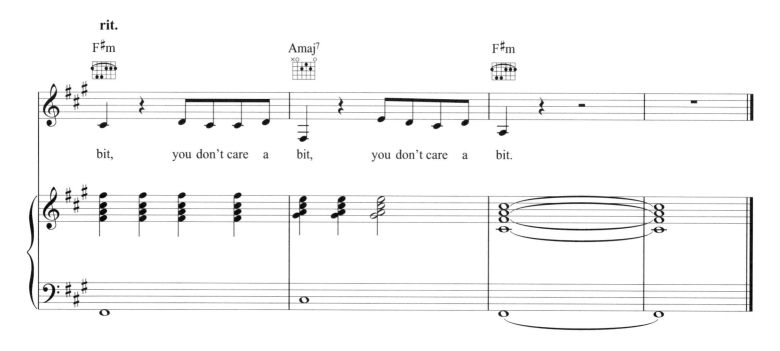

bit, you don't care a bit, you don't care a bit.

I'M KISSING YOU

Words & Music by Des'ree & Tim Atack.

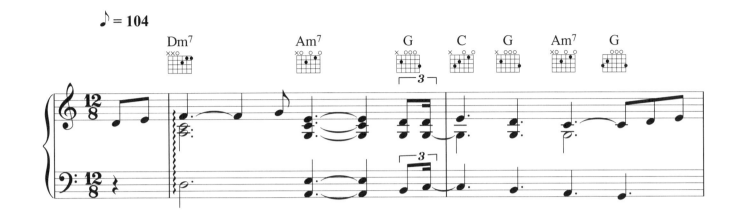

Mm. Hey, hey, hey. Pride can stand a thou-sand trials,

the strong will nev-er fall. But watch-ing stars with-out you, my

I WILL ALWAYS LOVE YOU

Words & Music by Dolly Parton.

IT'S NOT THAT EASY

Words & Music by
Lorne Tennant, Lars Jensen, Martin Larsson,
Sigurd Jansen & Glenn Tharaldsen.

IMAGINE

Words & Music by John Lennon.

1. I - ma-gine there's no Heav - en,
2. I - ma-gine there's no coun - tries,
3. I - ma-gine no po - ses - sions,

it's eas - y if you try.___
it is - n't hard to do.___
I won-der if you can.___

No hell be - low___
Noth - ing to kill or die___
No need for greed or hun -

NO ORDINARY LOVE

Words & Music by Adu & Matthewman.

LEAVE RIGHT NOW

Words & Music by Francis Eg White.

LET IT BE

Words & Music by John Lennon & Paul McCartney.

LOVE GOES DOWN

Words & Music by
Benjamin Drew, Eric Appapoulay,
Richard Cassell & Tom Goss.

1. I re-mem-ber when___ I___ was young and so___ were you.___
2. I re-mem-ber when___ I did you wrong, made___ you cry.___

All of___ the things___ we both said___
Made you feel so sad___ I knew I___

MAKE YOU FEEL MY LOVE

Words & Music by Bob Dylan.

NEW YORK

Words & Music by Paloma Faith & Jodi Marr.

days were long and the nights so cold, the pa-ges turned and the tale un-folds, he'd left me for an-oth - er la-
(2.) wolves they howled_ for my lost soul, I fell down a deep black hole, he'd left me for an-oth - er la-

- dy.   She stood so tall and she nev - er slept, there was not one mo - ment he could re - gret,_   he'd
- dy.   She poured the drinks and she poured the pow - er,   dia-mond girl_ who could talk for hours,   he'd

don't want to hear__ it. Your new laugh-ter lines,_____ I don't wan-na hear__ it. The

new - found friends she in - tro -duced___ you to,_____ I don't wan-na know__ them I just

wan-na be__ with you.__ Please don't make me go___ to_____ New__ York,_____

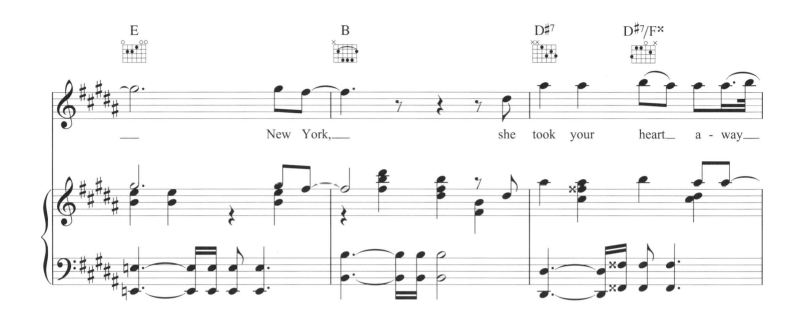

New York, ___ she took your heart___ a - way___

___ oh my. Her name was New___ York, ___ New York, ___ she

pois - oned your___ sweet mind.___ Her name was New___ York, ___ New_ York,___

NOTHING'S REAL BUT LOVE

Words & Music by Francis White & Rebecca Ferguson.

PARADISE

Words & Music by
Chris Martin, Guy Berryman, Jon Buckland,
Will Champion & Brian Eno.

THE SEA

Words & Music by Paul Godfrey, Ross Godfrey & Skye Edwards.

Liv-in' free.

Guitar

D.C. al Coda

Verse 2:
Fishing boats sail past the shore
No singing, may-day anymore
The sun is shining, the board is clear
Just you and I walk along the pier.

I left my soul *etc.*

Verse 3:
A cool breeze flows but mind the wasp
Some get stung, it's worth the cost
I'd love to stay, the city calls me home
More hassles, fuss and lies on the phone.

I left my soul *etc.*

SLOW

Words & Music by Sarah Joyce.

WHEREVER YOU WILL GO

Words & Music by Aaron Kamin & Alex Band.

A THOUSAND YEARS

Words & Music by David Hodges & Christina Perri.

1. Heart beats fast, col-ours and prom-is-es... How to be brave?_ How can I love when I'm a-fraid to fall? Watch-ing you

2. Time stands still, beau-ty in all she is... I will be brave._ I will not let an-y-thing take a-way what's stand-ing in

thou - sand years. I'll love you for a thou - sand more.

One step clo - ser,

WHEREVER YOU ARE

Music by Paul Mealor.

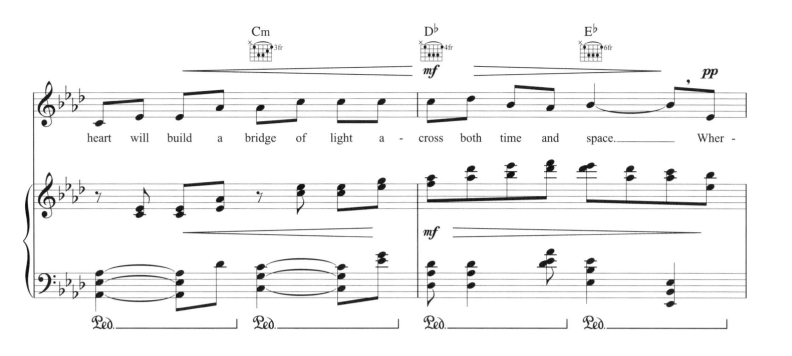

heart will build a bridge of light a - cross both time and space._____ Wher -

-ev - er you are,_____ our__ hearts still beat as one,_____ I

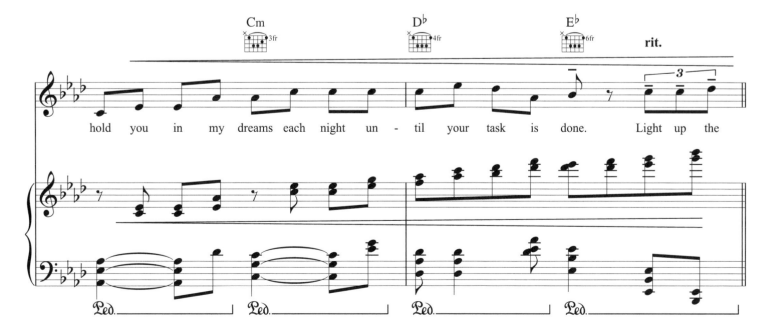

hold you in my dreams each night un - til your task is done. Light up the

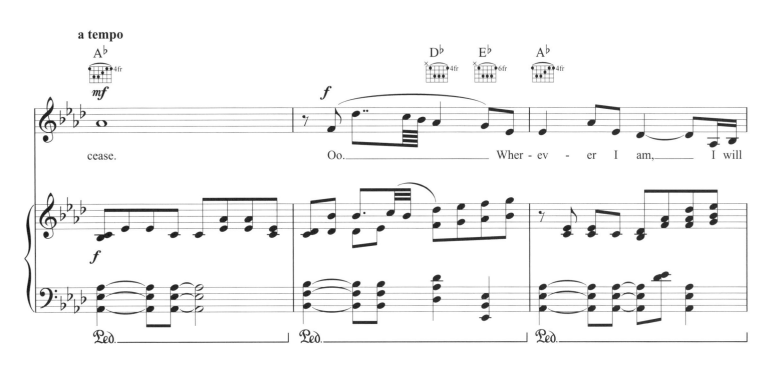

cease.   Oo.___   Wher - ev - er I am,___ I will

love you day by day,___   I will keep you safe, cling on to faith, a - long the dark, dark way.___ Wher -

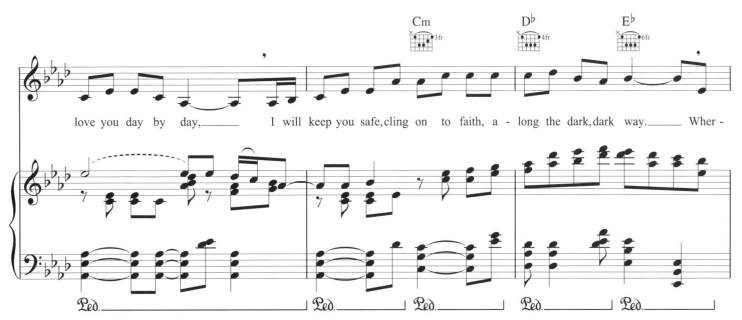

-ev - er I am,___   I will hold on through the night;___   I will

Lyrics:

pray each day, a safe re-turn, will look now to the light. Light up the

dark - ness, my won-drous star; Our__ hopes and dreams, my heart and yours, for-

-ev - er shin-ing far. Light up the dark - ness, my prince__ of

peace; May the stars shine all a-round you,may your cour - age___ nev - er

cease. Ah._____

Cou - rage nev - er_____ cease._____

YOUR SONG

Words & Music by Elton John & Bernie Taupin.

1. It's a lit-tle bit fun-ny, this feel-ing in-side.
2. So ex-cuse me for-get-ting, but these things I do.

I'm not one of those__ who__ can eas-i-ly hide.__
See, I've for-got-ten__ if they're green or they're blue.__

I don't have much mon-ey but boy, if I did
An-y-way the thing is, what I real-ly mean,

how won-der-ful life is now you're_____ in the world.

3. If I was a sculp-tor, but then a-gain, no. Or a girl__who makes po-tions__ in

a trav-el-ling show. I know it's not much, but it's the best I can do.

My gift__ is my song and__ this one is for you.__ Ah._____

YOU GIVE ME SOMETHING

Words & Music by James Morrison & Eg White.

1. You on-ly stay with me in the morn-ing,
2. You on-ly wait-ed up for hours,

you on-ly hold me when I sleep.
just to spend a lit-tle time a-lone with me.

23456789